little

mouse

likes to ask

BIG

questions.

Like
what is

higher

than the tallest giraffe?

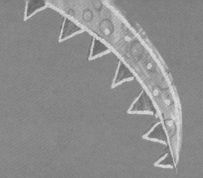

Longer

than a crocodile's tail ?

wiser

than the oldest owl ?

braver

than a roaring lion ?

wider

than a big blue whale?

Kinder

than a mother hen?

and **stronger**

than a herd of elephants ?

I know
what is

high
wide
Kind and
strong

brave
wise

and VERY
long ....

A prayer from Ephesians 3 verses 16-19.

May you know how **Wide** high long and **deep** the **love** of Christ **Jesus** is for **you!**